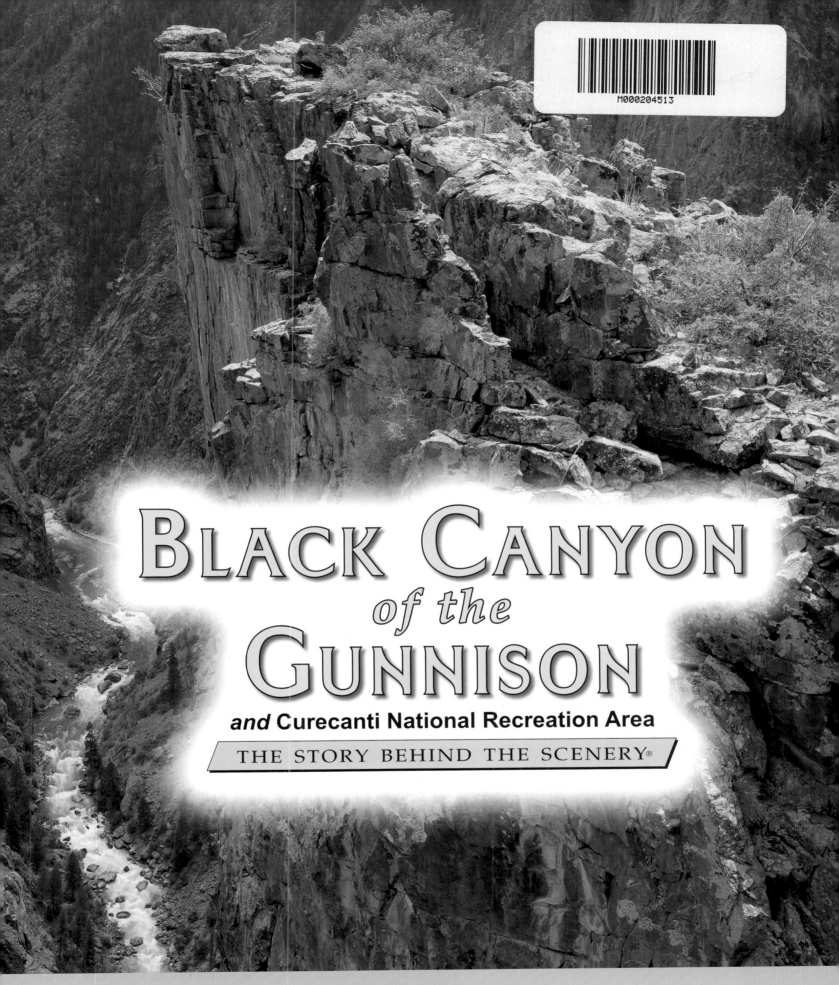

BLACK CANYON
of the
GUNNISON

and Curecanti National Recreation Area

THE STORY BEHIND THE SCENERY®

by Paul Zaenger

PAUL ZAENGER has a Bachelor of Science degree in Biology and has been an Interpretive Specialist at Black Canyon since 1993. Paul's other park assignments include: Death Valley National Park, Glen Canyon National Recreation Area and Mount Rushmore National Memorial.

Soaring cliffs and bellowing rapids reveal the constant struggle
between river and rock. The canyon endures to remind us that

change is always present in the natural world, but that it continues slowly, like a thousand years that pass by as an evening gone.

ED COOPER

No written record exists reflecting the thoughts of the earliest people to witness the chasm. Prehistoric hunters and gatherers, Utes, Spanish explorers, mountain men and trappers all passed by, but we will never know their thoughts on the tremendous cliffs. Through much of its length the canyon walls rise 2,000 feet from the river, the rapids pound at the river bed, and birds sail over the rims. Even today the canyon is a primeval wilderness much as it was thousands of years ago. It's easy to assume they were unmoved by the canyon's sheer scale, focusing only on survival. Yet, each of us today come to the precipice to behold the color, the drama and the depths, and to measure ourselves against this powerful scale of nature. Perhaps those of earlier generations did too.

The Painted Wall is the *highest cliff in Colorado at 2,250 feet above the river. The pink and white pegmatite stripes lace through the rock almost like lattice which seems to hold the wall in place.*

Black Canyon of the Gunnison National Park

The Great Pillars huddle together across the canyon from Gunnison Point and provide a testament to the chiseling effects of ice that wedges apart massive chunks of rock. This was once sedimentary rock, but deep in the earth it was cooked into a metamorphic rock called schist.

The Black Canyon of the Gunnison is steep and deep, with cliff walls that are both imposing and enduring. At the heart of the canyon lies the Gunnison River. With its buzz-saw action the river sliced through this aged rock, revealing eroded features that are both massive and intimate. Nearly 50 miles of the Gunnison River are protected in Black Canyon of the Gunnison National Park, Curecanti National Recreation Area, and the Gunnison Gorge National Conservation Area, each with a piece of the canyon, sharing a story that is woven together between them.

A parade of explorers has witnessed the river's power. Sometimes they forged ahead, sometimes they were turned back. Harnessed by three dams, the river is now controlled in Curecanti, but the weather cycles change – giving both dry and wet years, and the wet years have shown that it retains its strength when ample snow falls in the mountains of its basin.

Plants and animals have adapted to a life which a perpendicular world demands. Eagles, hawks and a host of other birds reign the skies. Evergreens, aspens and many other plants cling to the slopes which in turn offer shelter and survival for the multitude of animals that call these areas home.

LAURENCE PARENT

Late afternoon sun gilds the slopes and mesas that surround Blue Mesa Reservoir. The waters of Blue Mesa soothe both body and soul in the hours before twilight.

The canyon holds a vertical wilderness, rugged to an extreme, and offers intense challenges for climbers, river runners, anglers and hikers. Yet there is adventure for everyone who comes here to match their abilities with the demands that are offered. From the rim, part way into the canyon, or from the river the opportunities to witness the canyon's power and grandeur are endless.

JEFF ACHEY

More than resolute courage is needed to scale the cliffs like this climber on North Chasm View Wall. Regardless of the route, good preparation, equipment, and stamina are all factors of a successful climb. A cool head and good judgment are crucial when conditions, such as weather, rock fall, or malfunctioning equipment, come into play. Many come for such an adventure, but this isn't a good place for beginners. The extreme wilderness conditions and world-class climbs make this canyon a breath-taking challenge.

Stop at any overlook. No matter where you are you'll hear the muffled roar of the river. Only such a river could bring about a canyon like this.

Recipe for a Canyon

LAURENCE PARENT

Rock moves. We don't usually think about it, but earthquakes are a continuing reminder that rock moves, and that it moves on a big scale. The geologic premise of plate tectonics tells us that earth's crust is made of large, relatively thin, plates of rock that are constantly but slowly moving. They sometimes collide, and sometimes pull apart, scrape side-to-side, or one block overrides another. But rock moves. To understand how the bulk of Black Canyon rock came about we need to picture a moving mass of rock being lowered deep into the earth.

METAMORPHOSIS

Consider a pan of brownies fresh from the oven. Instead of letting the pan cool, let's put the pan back into the oven, turn up the heat a couple thousand degrees and continue baking for a long time. The result is the transformation from brownies into something we wouldn't recognize.

That's what happened here, geologically speaking. A mass of rock was lowered deep into the earth. Layers and layers of rock were deposited onto it. Perhaps oceans covered it. Little by little the mass is lowered deeper and deeper. Eventually it is deep enough that intense pressures and temperatures are applied to the rock, but not so extreme that the rock

Pinnacles come in many shapes and sizes.
This one projects near the top of Long Draw. Early morning shadows darken this cleft that descends to the river. The main chasm is often in shadow, which contributes to the name Black Canyon.

LISA LYNCH

Douglas-fir trees and a host of shrubs *grapple with the eroding rock near Island Peaks View. Ice has been chipping away space for seeds to get a start. Flat-top columns offer ledges for shrubs to gain a foot-hold, while large clefts provide homes for trees. Canyon rims that range from 7,700 feet to 8,500 feet in elevation are just high enough to wring out rain and snow from the atmosphere to support vegetation usually found in higher terrain. The roots apply ever increasing pressure against the rock to force more erosion.*

melts. When the rock is six to eight miles below the surface, it is under such high pressures and temperatures that, like our pan of brownies, it is literally baked into something altogether different. This is the origin of metamorphic rock. Metamorphose: to change; and this process resulted in the rock of Black Canyon of the Gunnison.

The temperature and pressure levels can vary, and our mass of rock was tilted so that some of it was lower than the rest. When different amounts of pressure or temperature are added, we usually end up with a different kind of rock. Lower temperatures and pressures result in a finer grain rock called

WILLARD CLAY

Most of the steep cliffs of the canyon are on the sunny north side and the slopes are on the shady south side. Snow and rain remain longer on the south side, wearing away the cliffs more quickly. The north side erodes slowly due to the drying action of the sun's rays. So the Painted Wall, North Chasm View Wall, Tablets of Moses I and II, and these cliffs near Balanced Rock View persist against the elements.

schist. The crystals of this rock are tiny and closer together in part because the rock hasn't been under as much strain. But when the rock is lowered deeper, the pressures from above and the temperatures from below begin to rise. The rock becomes more like a thick jelly or jam. This mushy jam-like mixture results in a more coarse-grained rock called gneiss (pronounced 'nice') with crystals that tend to be larger. This process is not exact, leading to rocks with varying crystals blended together.

It isn't possible to say what the original rock was before the heating and pressure changed them.

Like brownies, if you change the ingredients you will get a different result. Various rock types lead to a variety of metamorphic stone, and minerals in some of these Black Canyon rocks suggest that they were once sedimentary. In other locations it appears that the rock was of igneous origin, a lava flow or layer of ash. In any case, millions of years went by after these precursor rocks were originally formed before they were lowered into the pressure cooker of the earth. We will never know the age of those original rocks, but geologists use radiometric methods to place an approximate age for the metamorphic rocks in Black Canyon at 1.7 billion years.

MAGMA ON THE MOVE

Later, molten rock coming up from below intruded into the schist and gneiss in a couple ways. While our metamorphic rocks were still deep below earth's surface, large blobs or bodies of magma, called plutons, advanced on them. Slowly they pushed into the vicinity of the schist and gneiss; sometimes melting the existing rocks as they advanced, sometimes yanking the rocks along the side, folding them into the mix like chocolate chips. Three different plutons miles apart advanced from below, yielding a granite-like rock called monzonite.

Still later, more magma intruded into all of this rock. The additional ingredient of water in this magma caused its injection to be different. In small amounts, the water made the magma a little more fluid so it didn't swallow everything in its path like the plutons. Instead it oozed and squeezed into the existing schist, gneiss, or the monzonite like jelly infused into a jelly roll. It penetrated every weakness, fault or crack in the rocks. Sometimes it flowed in straight patterns. Sometimes it bored through the rocks pervading and dominating them. Rich in potassium, this magma also cooled slowly and formed pegmatite. Because all of this rock was formed deep in the earth, as in the cellar of a home and is so very old, geologists refer to is as base or basement rock.

ADDING A LAYER CAKE

The Black Canyon is situated at the eastern end of the Colorado Plateau. The plateau sprawls over much of the Four Corners states of Arizona, Colorado, New Mexico and Utah and is loaded with enchanting panoramas. The Plateau is known for its colorful layers of rock laid down over the eons by shallow seas, meandering rivers and gigantic sand dunes. The Precambrian rock of the Black Canyon that had been buried was eventually uplifted to the earth's surface where some of the sediments of the Plateau were deposited upon it.

ED COOPER

High heat and pressure baked sedimentary rock deep in the earth to form the ruddy red metamorphic gneiss of the Painted Wall. Like oozing toothpaste, magma squeezed its way into the gneiss forming the stripes of pegmatite when the magma cooled. Geologic forces occur in three dimensions so the stripes could be wider as they penetrate into the cliff face, or they could pinch out altogether. The only way to know would be to cut a slice off of the wall. Many shapes could be spotted in the stripes, but the upper lines seem to form dragons or serpents. The snout of the upper monster reaches to the top of the wall to form Serpent Point.

Morning mists are scattered by the rising sun along the Rim Rock Trail. The cliffs in the distance are near Cimarron as the Gunnison River winds its way underneath the watchful stance of Poverty Mesa, Coffee Pot Hill, and Black Mesa in Curecanti National Recreation Area.

Imagine that we place one layer of cake after another on the pan of brownies. Likewise, one sedimentary formation after another was placed on top of the metamorphic rock. The environments changed over time, so the layers of rock also changed. A giant layer of sand dunes initially sat on top of the rocks forming a layer now called Entrada Sandstone. Other layers followed; the Wanaka Formation, the Morrison Formation, the Dakota Sandstone, Mancos Shale, all very visible in the Gunnison Gorge National Conservation Area. This layering of rock came to an end as the great mountain building period, the Laramide Orogeny, began.

Over a period of millions of years the Rocky Mountains were pushed up, and the basement rock of Black Canyon with its sedimentary layers on top was uplifted, too. Streams draining the newly formed Rockies east of the canyon coursed across the Gunnison Uplift eroding off the very top sedimentary layers. The melting snow in the mountains gradually gathered to give birth to the Gunnison River.

Perhaps more layers would have been removed, but volcanoes that exploded to the north and south intruded on the scene. Repeated volcanic eruptions and lava flows at the center of the West Elk Mountains melted ice and snow, and triggered huge mud flows. The flows constantly repeated and temporarily blocked the river, but time and again it broke through the rock and continued its course westward to the sea.

Put your thumb over an open bottle of soda and shake it. Move your thumb and the pop explodes out of the bottle. The massive volcanoes of the San Juan Mountains to the south belched ash, rock bombs, and lava thousands of feet into the air in much the same way. The volcanoes repeatedly blasted this material skyward, placing layer upon layer of ash over the uplift, like icing on the cake. Again the river would be blocked, but just the same it would break through before another series of outbursts placed more ash on the scene.

This continued for millions of years before the volcanoes finally went silent, but they had a profound effect on the river. With each succeeding eruption the ash pushed the river farther north, and positioned the river over the Precambrian rock. Precise placement of the river was critical as it began carving through the upper layers, or there would be no Black Canyon today.

A Master Sculptor

Stop at any overlook. No matter where you are you'll hear the muffled roar of the river. Go down to the river, though, and it's noisy, forceful and turbulent. Only such a river could bring about a canyon like this.

As time ebbed and flowed, glaciers came and went. While there is no evidence of glaciers in the canyon, there is ample evidence of them in the

It's hard to find a river in North America that drops in elevation more rapidly through its canyon than the Gunnison. The river falls an average of 43 feet per mile through all of the Black Canyon, but in this two mile stretch, the Gunnison descends 480 feet. The Colorado River in Grand Canyon averages seven feet per mile. Only the Yellowstone River in Wyoming has a steeper gradient.

mountains of the Gunnison River Basin. During the periods of cooling, glaciers formed, and the river had less water to do its cutting. But during times of warming and melting, glaciers would have supplied immense volumes of water to the river, creating colossal floods. Geologists estimate that a river can do more slicing in one fantastic deluge than in 50 years of average flow. It is the moving of debris by the river that is actually doing the carving. Like liquid sandpaper, the Gunnison chews and grinds its way year after year into the gorge.

This powerful force we call the Gunnison chiseled down through our frosting of ash, and layer cake of sedimentary rock, leaving canyon walls above it in which it was confined. In time it began cutting into the harder crystalline rock of schist, gneiss and granites. By then it was hemmed in by its own canyon walls. When it came to the older more defiant stone it had no alternative but to continue cutting. Such streams are said to be superimposed upon a more resistant rock.

While the Gunnison was scouring away at the harder, crystalline rocks, the nearby North Fork and Uncompahgre Rivers, which drain into the Gunnison downstream from the gorge, were cutting into the softer Mancos Shale. The shale was easier to slice through so these rivers created open valleys and lowered the elevation of their beds faster than the Gunnison could. As time wore on, the end of the canyon became lower and lower, causing the fall of the river to become greater and greater. Not only was there the push of the river from the flooding of melting glaciers and snow, but there was the pull of the river at the end of the canyon causing the river to increase its slope.

The pace of carving by the river was no match for the surrounding side streams. Only a few had the water supply to cut through as side canyons of the gorge. Most of the others were either left hanging, their valleys suspended well above the flow, or they result in very narrow gashes usually because they are along one of a number of faults in the rock.

Even as most side streams can't keep pace with the carving power of the river, the weathering process that is sculpting the cliffs is also slow. Lichens, a combination of algae and fungus, start this process, providing a chemical break-down of the "glue" that holds the grains and crystals of rock together. Cracks form, and from season to season rain and snow blow into the cracks and fissures in the canyon walls. As temperatures drop the moisture freezes and expands, applying pressure against all angles of the rock. The resistant rock in the cliffs eventually weakens and breaks, the rubble falling into the canyon for the river to haul away.

The sun plays a great part in this as low angles of the winter rays have trouble reaching the snow that piles up on the south side. Moisture lingers on the south side, eroding the rocks more rapidly, and moderating the steepness of the slopes. The north

WILLARD CLAY

The power of the Gunnison River becomes manifest when it floods. Although controlled by dams upstream, a heavy snowpack in the mountains can still cause a deluge. With the additional power the river can push loads of sediment and roll huge boulders. Geologists estimate that a river will cut more during one torrent than in 50 years of average flow.

LISA LYNCH

The erosion process begins with lichens.
Formed by a union of a fungus and algae, these organisms begin weathering the cliffs by breaking down the chemical bonds of minerals within the rock.

side receives the sun's rays more directly all year. The snow thaws more quickly, sometimes evaporating rather than melting. Erosion at work on the walls of the canyon isn't able to keep pace with the cutting power of the river to deepen the canyon. The narrow tight and steep cliffs create many shadows, leaving much of the cleft dark, even in the summer. And so it has come to be called Black Canyon.

The river is oblivious to time. For two million years it has been at work slicing, grinding and churning away at the crystalline rocks below. Some ask how far down into the earth the rock descends. It hasn't been drilled, so we don't know, but the potential is great. Yet, the erosion process continues on, and it becomes difficult for us to perceive changes in the canyon. Our moment in time is too brief.

SUGGESTED READING

HANSEN, WALLACE R. *The Black Canyon of the Gunnison, In Depth.* Tucson, Arizona: Southwest Parks and Monuments Association, 1987.

PRATHER, THOMAS. *Geology of the Gunnison Country.* Gunnison, Colorado: B & B Printers, Incorporated, 1982.

DIXON, DOUGAL. *The Practical Geologist.* New York, New York: Simon & Schuster, Incorporated, 1992.

KIOUS, W.J. AND TILLING, R.I. *This Dynamic Earth: The Story of Plate Tectonics.* Denver, Colorado: United States Geological Survey, 1996.

SUGGESTED WEB SITES

http://coloradogeologicalsurvey.org
https://www.yourwatercolorado.org

ED COOPER

Many slabs are precariously perched on the face of the canyon, and it seems only a breeze could topple them into the depths.
The process of rock slabs splitting off the cliffs is called exfoliation. Rock falls are rarely witnessed, but when they roar to the canyon floor the river has more rubble for carving away at its bed. The boulders pile up in places, causing the river to twist its way through the sieve. Floods will remove the debris, in time, but nearly as quickly the cliffs will send more for the river to haul away.

Hidden from visitors to the south rim, these streaks descend along the cliff below Chasm View. This is desert varnish; a mixture of iron and manganese oxides concentrated there by bacteria furnished with water streaming down the wall. Although it is commonly found on cliff faces in the Four-Corners Region, there are only a few examples of the varnish scattered in the canyon.

LISA LYNCH

A view of the Narrows can be found at the bottom of an arduous hike down Long Draw. This place is the tightest pinch the river tolerates between the canyon walls. The Narrows are about 1,750 feet below the rim where the cliffs are separated by only 40 feet.

ED COOPER

LAURENCE PARENT

Geologic plate movements on a large scale can be revealed in small ways. As ancient tectonic plates collided to form the North American continent, the force of the impact caused smaller rock fracture zones. Erosion has cut through these fractures revealing spires and columns seen at Cross Fissures View. Though geologically small, the columns tell of the great power of plate tectonics.

Life in a vertical world offers challenges and opportunities. From Blue Mesa Reservoir down through the gorge, plants and animals give testimony to the success of their adaptations.

Life on the Edge

The trail to Painted Wall View offers an *explosion of spring wildflowers. Scattered among the sagebrush are the orange-red Indian paintbrush and bright yellow arrowleaf balsamroot. Flowers are abundant with plenty of rain, and the balsamroot blooms in open areas from Blue Mesa Reservoir to the Gunnison Gorge. The woody balsam-flavored roots were a food source for the American Indians.*

JACK OLSON

Life Among the Cliffs

Any season offers discovery among the plants and animals. Spring brings a wildflower display in the open grasslands, and under the canopy of the forests. The skies reverberate with the gurgling chorus of the sandhill cranes circling overhead as they fly north. Other migrating birds add a splash of color to the air, some nesting near or in the canyon.

Swifts and swallows, seen throughout the parks, swoop and dive on early summer mornings. Walk a trail to take in the fragrance of the pinyon pines and juniper trees. Most animals find shade in the heat of the day, but watch for a soaring hawk, or a silent bobcat in the evenings.

Fall is announced by vibrant colors, and chill breezes flutter aspen leaves. An immense silence envelops the landscape. Winter snows present harsh challenges to wildlife, their tracks divulging their activities. Elk, bobcats, rabbits and coyotes are all tramping through the snow, keeping warm, finding food and waiting for the coming spring. This cycle continues, year after year.

LISA LYNCH

Bald Eagles winter in the canyon and along the shores of Blue Mesa Reservoir until the lake freezes over. Spotting one flying over the reservoir or soaring over the canyon is a thrill. Other birds of prey include the Peregrine Falcon which is an unrivaled hunter within the canyon.

LISA LYNCH

The Rocky Mountain penstemon thrives in full sun, and grows on the slopes around Blue Mesa Lake. It loves open areas along the canyon rims, and is known for growing among pinyon pines and juniper trees. It produces nectar twice each day, timed specifically to attract preferred pollinators.

Clusters of golden sulphurflower do well in poor or shallow soils, so the rocky rims and cliffs of the canyon are natural habitat. Blooms occur in early or mid-summer, then turn deep crimson when the flower heads go to seed.

JEFF GNASS

LISA LYNCH

Foxtail barley is one of the many grasses that stitch together the soils and open areas of the rims and mesas of the parks. Abundant grasses are an indication of good health in the ecosystem, and are important forage for wildlife. However, once the foxtail has gone to seed, its bristles make it inedible.

LISA LYNCH

The western red columbine, *Aquilegia elegantula*, is a close relative of the Colorado state flower. A member of the Buttercup family, the deep spurs of the flower store nectar to entice pollinators to reach the back of the blossom.

The juniper trees at Dragon Point are unusually contorted and twisted. These trees can grow in impossible conditions including heat and drought, and their shaggy bark can withstand the ferocious gales that whip along the rim. Its bark has been used by Utes for making rope, sandals and clothing, and the berries for food.

Waning daylight and the chilly fall weather coax the aspens to turn golden. Groves of these trees are tucked into the slopes of the canyon, and blanket the mesas along Colorado Highway 92. Ambling among them offers an ease to life that natural solitude can give.

The Gunnison's prairie dog is called a keystone
species, meaning that many other animals depend on
it for survival. Eagles, bobcats, foxes and snakes are
among the many that would struggle without it.

LISA LYNCH

Many researchers agree that the
Gunnison Grouse is a unique species though a
close relative of the Greater Sage-Grouse. Its
habitat is limited, but it is an important contributor
to the biodiversity of the parks.

LISA LYNCH

LISA LYNCH

The scarlet flowers of the claret cup cactus are easy to spot, particularly because the
plants can be huge. In some places there will be clumps of hundreds of stems. They thrive in
dry areas of the parks, even on the cliffs, with blossoms in late spring or early summer.

A mule deer emerges after the heat of a summer's day to browse. They have excellent hearing enhanced by the funnel-shaped ears, making it possible to sense danger before smelling or seeing it. They can also bounce as they run, called stotting or pronking, which further helps them elude predators.

STEPHEN TRIMBLE

LAURENCE PARENT

The soft light at sunset is a surprising contrast to the struggle many plants have to survive jammed into the cracks and fissures of the cliffs.

SUGGESTED READING

FAGAN, DAMIAN. *Canyon Country Wildflowers.* Helena MONTANA: FALCON PRESS, 1988.

KERSHAW, LINDA, ANDY BEZENER. *Rocky Mountain Nature Guide.* Lone Pine Publishing, Auburn, WA, 1999.

LANNER, RONALD M. *The Pinyon Pine, A Natural and Cultural History.* University of Nevada Press, Reno, NV, 1981.

RIGHTER, ROBERT, RICH LEVAD, DEXTER COEN, AND KIM POTTER. *Birds of Western Colorado Plateau and Mesa Country.* Grand Valley Audubon Society, Grand Junction, CO 2004.

SUGGESTED WEB SITES

www.siskadee.org
www.herbariumbiologycolostate.edu

Overleaf: *Sailboats ride the waves of Blue Mesa Reservoir near Dillon Pinnacles. Photo by Lisa Lynch.*

*In places the current would sweep them away
so quickly they had to struggle
to stay out of the rapids. In others the flow
would slam them into treacherous rocks.*

Plumbing the Depths

People have been stymied by the Black Canyon for centuries. In fact, some of the oldest workings of humans in North America have been found by archaeologists along the Gunnison River. Many people who inhabited the western slope of Colorado tried to extract sustenance from the land. Yet whether very old or in recent times they have always had trouble taking on the impassable character of the canyon.

The first people to live in the Gunnison Basin survived an unsteady existence. The oldest signs of their touch on the land came during the Folsom period when hunters created wide spear points to subdue large mammals. As the climate evolved, they did, too. Later, archaic people began to make widespread use of the basin, and especially the lands around present day Blue Mesa Reservoir in

A *few species of Indian paintbrush bloom in the parks. Their roots will attach to the roots of nearby plants to suck nutrients from the host. While they can make their own food, they thrive more as parasites.*

LISA LYNCH

Curecanti National Recreation Area, adapting from generation to generation for some 8,000 years.

The Utes eventually migrated into Colorado, following game and making use of the land. The introduction of the horse by the Spanish made hunting much more efficient and allowed them to make greater use of the resources along the canyon rims. Little is known, though, about Ute relationships with the canyon beyond their physical needs. Settlers moved in, and by 1882 most of the Utes were moved west into Utah.

THE COMING EUROPEANS

In 1853 Captain John Gunnison led a military survey looking for a railroad route linking the eastern United States with the Pacific. His expedition was the first to record the nature of the gorge, and though he saw only the upper reaches of the canyon, the river was later named for him. The 1870s witnessed the Hayden Survey of Colorado, and while a few laborers of the survey were lowered down among the ledges, the most they could report was that the canyon was inaccessible.

A flood of miners hoped to cash in on gold found in the nearby mountains. The surge of people brought a demand for goods and services which was met by railroad entrepreneur, William Jackson Palmer.

ED COOPER

The Ute term for the canyon is Tomichi (toe.MEE.chee), which roughly translates to "land of high cliffs and water." They hunted and gathered along the rims, and migrated through to the high country. The local band of Utes called themselves Tabeguache (TA.beh.wash), or "people who live on the warm side of the mountain."

Hikers on the Gunnison Route will see many features on their venture to the river. The quest is a grueling skid going down and a rock-tripping, root-grabbing scramble to the rim. This thumb of rock is across the river from the camp sites.

KIRKENDALL-SPRING

In order to overcome the difficulties of the Colorado terrain, Palmer deemed his railroad should use the narrow gauge width between the wheels (3 feet) common in Europe. He was able to reach the town of Gunnison from Pueblo in 1881 before any competing railroads, and then immediately pushed the rails west into the Black Canyon. This tortuous route in the depths of the canyon turned out to be some of the most difficult and costly construction for the company. When the railhead reached a break in the cliffs, cut by the Cimarron River, crews erected the town of Cimarron.

Palmer wanted to extend the line downstream through the canyon to the town of Delta and directed a survey to study the chasm. Led by Byron Bryant, the team spent the winter months doing their job only to report that the river route was financially impractical. The railroad went over Cerro Summit, around the south side of the canyon to Montrose, and Cimarron became an important rail town, providing a critical link along the line.

RECLAMATION ENTERS THE SCENE

As mining began to taper off as a mainstay of the local economy, farmers in the nearby Uncompahgre (un.com.PAH.grey) Valley were seeking ways to secure water to irrigate their crops. They looked to the Gunnison River as a viable source. The problem was the gigantic canyon holding the Gunnison's waters, but in 1900 John Pelton formed a group to explore the canyon and find a point where a tunnel could be dug.

They put in at Cimarron amid a great deal of hope, but shortly after starting they met disaster when one of their boats crashed into one of the jagged rocks of the river. They abandoned the wreck and moved downstream, hauling the remaining craft around many serious rapids. They had expected the trip to last about a week, but the exhausting work delayed their plans.

Conditions worsened as a storm brought bone-chilling rain, their provisions ran low, and they continued to risk injury, constantly dragging the boat over the boulders. They eventually came to a spot called the Narrows, where the river separates the cliffs by only 40 feet. Evaluating their situation, they elected to climb to the rim rather than risk the unknown.

Though defeated, the group gained a great deal of attention. From Washington, D.C., the U.S. Geological Survey telegrammed Colorado State Hydrographer Abraham Lincoln Fellows to investigate.

LISA LYNCH

Of his 1901 trip through the canyon Fellows wrote, *"Again… there might be a deep pool where we were obliged to swim, into which the water boiled from the caves above and sucked out again through the crevices below. In one of these pools I was drawn completely under,… but by the dint of the hardest kind of swimming, succeeded in getting into still water."*

Fellows had learned practical use of irrigation systems traveling the state, and he quickly tapped William Torrence, from the previous expedition, as an assistant for another trip in 1901.

Rather than taking a heavy boat and provisions, Fellows proposed using an inflatable rubber air mattress, normally used for sleeping to make river crossings, and asked mule skinner Wilbur Dillon to supply their. Being dropped off the train at Cimarron, a fellow traveler remarked that she was glad the conductor "put those two tramps off the train".

They made their way quickly down canyon, and upon seeing the Narrows they paused to consider their fate.

Perhaps swallowing his fear, Fellows plunged into the river, keeping as close to the cliff as possible. In minutes he was washed up on the rocky shore of the other side, followed immediately by Torrence.

Once beyond the Narrows, the journey became more tortuous. In places the current would sweep them so quickly they had to struggle to stay out of the rapids. In others the flow would slam them into treacherous rocks.

Through their ten-day excursion and some additional surveying, the location was finalized. Excavation began on the six-mile Gunnison Tunnel in 1905. They worked from both ends, digging at East Portal in the canyon, and the town of Lujane on the

ED COOPER

R*everend Mark* *Warner, park founder, gave the names to many of the canyon's features. Perhaps he was thinking of the Kneeling Camel when he wrote, "Towers, pinnacles, spires and other fantastic rock formations greet the eye with an ever new challenge, as sunshine and shadow play their part in the creation of this ever changing pageant of rugged grandeur and majestic beauty."*

Colorado
Highway 92 crosses over Blue Mesa Dam, one of three within Curecanti National Recreation Area. Completed in 1965, the earthen fill dam is 390 feet high and more water is stored behind it than any other reservoir in the state.

LISA LYNCH

valley side. Ditches and canals were also under construction in the valley when, amid great fanfare and a presidential visit by William Howard Taft, the tunnel was dedicated in 1909.

Throughout the 20th century reclamation has played a role in the Gunnison Basin. In later years Blue Mesa, Morrow Point and Crystal Dams were built. They are managed together in Curecanti National Recreation Area to provide water storage, flood control and produce electricity.

THE CHASM'S CHALLENGE

Not long after the fields in the Uncompahgre Valley began to receive water from the Gunnison some started to look at the river and canyon in a different way. The canyon offered unique beauty and recreation that couldn't be found elsewhere. One of the first to see the canyon in this light was a young river runner, Ellsworth Kolb.

Kolb was one of the most determined explorers intent on enduring all that the river had to dish out. After many excursions in Grand Canyon he set out in 1916 to take on the Gunnison, and film the adventure in the process.

A crowd gathered to see his group off at Cimarron, but after drifting into the current he was taken up into the rapid with a "perpendicular whirlpool" that caught him like a bucking bronco. After managing for a moment or two, he was thrown out into the churning waters. In spite of the obstacles the group continued downriver with their other boats, but after several frustrating days they hiked out.

Not to be thwarted, Kolb met up with longtime river runner Bert Loper. They chose heavy, 250 pound wooden boats, like the ones used in Grand Canyon, to make the run. That October they quickly floated from Cimarron to the Gunnison Tunnel, and just for fun they piled all of their gear, a lantern, and the East Portal caretaker into one of the boats and floated through the tunnel. The act brought headlines and chuckles all around western Colorado.

Turning again to the river, they met continuous trouble, once dynamiting the rocks to free a jammed boat. When they reached the Narrows, they both suffered injuries after a wet heavy snow. They gobbled down the last of their provisions in agony and clawed their way to the canyon rim.

Kolb came back to the river two more times that fall with anyone he could find to continue the journey, but he finally gave up in early December, vowing to rejoin the challenge the following summer. Through his persistence Kolb demonstrated

JEFF GNASS

On a survey for the Denver and Rio Grande Railroad, transitman Harvey Wright wrote, "Here to was unfolded view after view of the most wonderful, the most thrilling of rock exposures, one vanishing from view only to be replaced by another still more imposing. A view which could easily be made into a Scottish Castle would be followed by another suggesting the wildest parts of the most imposing height and majestic proportions."

Through contributions and partnerships, the South Rim Visitor Center was built in 1998. In a dedication with dignitaries that was honored with descendants of canyon explorers, it was committed to function as a place for visitors to learn of the canyon and share their adventures and experiences. It serves as part warming hut in the winter, and part breezeway in the summer, but all enjoy the knotty, lodgepole pine construction.

DAMON PACE

that hidden in the Black Canyon was treasure in its beauty and recreation potential beyond the monetary gain earlier explorers had hoped to find.

Montrose minister Mark Warner was not large or burly as previous explorers, but he was an avid outdoorsman who loved to fish, hunt, and hike. He and others built a fire of excitement in the Montrose Lions Club to construct a road out to the edge of the canyon at what is today's Chasm View. They finished their work in 1930, and though it was not very refined, the route did allow travelers to peek into the depths for the first time. The new road brought many people, but it also left the canyon vulnerable to exploitation.

Warner waded into the political waters to convince state and federal leaders that the canyon was a jewel to be saved, and it was proclaimed a National Monument by President Herbert Hoover in 1933. Warner assisted in the management of the new monument through its early years, establishing trails, new overlooks and a road for the north rim.

It was then that he suggested to local Congressman Edward Taylor that perhaps the monument should be enlarged and made a National Park, but his proposal would have to wait for some 60 years.

SUGGESTED READING

BARTLETT, R.A. AND GOETZMANN, W.H. *Exploring the American West, 1803-1879.* Washington, D.C.: National Park Service, 1982.

CARMICHAEL, TESS. *Let's Make the Desert Bloom: The Uncompahgre Project, 1890-1909.* Journal of the Western Slope, v. 8, n. 4, pp1-32, Fall 1993.

CASSELLS, E. STEVE. *The Archaeology of Colorado.* Boulder, Colorado: Johnson Printing, 1983.

REISNER, MARC. *Cadillac Desert.* New York, New York: Penguin Books, USA, 1986.

VANDENBUSCHE, DUANE. *The Gunnison Country.* Gunnison, Colorado: B & B Printers, Incorporated, 1980.

SUGGESTED WEB SITES

www.historycolorado.org

JEFF ACHEY

Climbing at Black Canyon of the Gunnison

For many climbers, the challenges at Black Canyon, or "The Black" as they have come to call it, are unequaled in North America except at Yosemite National Park. The canyon was difficult to reach in the 1960s, but one young man, Layton Kor, was determined to experience it through the exciting and growing sport. In 1962 he became the first to establish a climbing route in the canyon.

He would sometimes cajole friends to join him in pioneering climbs throughout the 60's, and he gained a reputation of extraordinary first ascents. Many other climbers have followed, establishing most routes on North and South Chasm View Walls and the buttresses and main face of the Painted Wall.

Climbers do this to test their physical endurance, the thrill of hanging on a wall, or to take a break from our frantic world. But whatever the reason, they achieve a sort of communion between themselves, the rock and the sky.

Suspended high above the river on The Nose route, climbers ascend the eastern corner of North Chasm View Wall. Several attempts were made at this section of cliff, but Earl Wiggins and Bryan Becker reached the rim in 1978. Shade gives climbers a break from the intense heat of the sun and radiation from the cliff.

JEFF ACHEY

After making a first ascent, climbers give a name to the route. Some of these are as colorful as they are, with titles like No Pig Left, Journey through Mirkwood, Astro Dog, Stratosfear, and Veterans with Vertigo. This climber is on Hallucinogen Wall, a section of North Chasm View Wall.

*Fishing, swimming, boating, and windsurfing
are popular activities found at Curecanti. Look
deeper, though, and the secrets of this recreation
area will unfold in a delightful surprise.*

The Recreation Area Experience

Curecanti

The historical spelling of Curecanti (Kur. eh. CAHN.tee) has several variations, but the Ute elder Curecanti, was involved with negotiations over tribal lands in the years following the Civil War. He was at once congenial, and a roust-about, and with his twin brother participated in ceremonial bear dances. The land survey of Colorado led by Ferdinand V. Hayden in the early 1870s named a stream that drained into the canyon for Curecanti. Later, the huge obelisk of rock across the river from its mouth was named for him, as well.

This same Curecanti Creek taps the high peaks of the West Elk Mountains, and splashes life-giving waters to plants and animals on its cascade into the canyon. Streams to the bottom of the canyon are rare, but provide excitement to a hiker.

The lands of the recreation area poised as a transition zone of life, lodged between the Rocky Mountains upstream and the Plateau Country to the west. Open sage brush flats surround Blue Mesa Reservoir with groves of Douglas-fir and aspen gathered close by. Forests crowd the rims of the canyon and charge down its slopes above Morrow Point Reservoir gradually giving way to Gambel oaks, and serviceberry bushes above Crystal Reservoir to the west.

While this area is best known for Blue Mesa Lake, exploring the nooks and crannies of its many treasures will enrich one's wild adventures and soothe the turmoil from our fast-paced lifestyle with solitude and beauty.

JACK OLSON

Perhaps nothing is *so lovely as waking up in the morning on Blue Mesa Lake. Sailors use care in the afternoon winds as they can be very brisk.*

***V**isitors experience the* steep cliffs and canyon habitat on a boat tour of Morrow Point Reservoir. The ranger-guided trip reveals forested slopes, soaring eagles, Chipeta Falls, and unfolds prominent scenes of the Denver & Rio Grande Railroad which ran in the upper part of Black Canyon.

***T**he one-mile Pine Creek Trail follows the cascading stream and offers an* intimate encounter with the canyon. The walk follows the old railroad bed of the Denver & Rio Grande line, provides a close-up look of the Douglas-fir forest, and winds up at the dock for the boat tour of Morrow Point Lake.

The Curecanti Needle rockets out of
the waters of Morrow Point Reservoir.
Its granite-like rock has withstood the elements and the power of running water. Faults, or lines
of weakness in the rock, have made the monolith distinct. A large crack from the left was exploited
by Blue Creek to rip down that side of the pinnacle. Fissures have been at work behind the tower to isolate the far
side, and the Gunnison slashed its main channel down the middle to put the spire into an impressive prominence.
The needle became one of the best known landmarks on the railroad, and was used in the company logo.

LISA LYNCH

S*till waters reflect*
the Precambrian cliffs
which are across from Wilson's Landing. This exposure of metamorphic rock found in
the Gunnison Canyon at the upper end of Blue Mesa Reservoir is isolated from the rest of
the rock of Black Canyon. Anglers often try their luck in this favored fishing venue.

LISA LYNCH

The Gunnison River meanders from the town of Gunnison to Blue Mesa Lake. The riparian, or river, habitat abounds with plant and wildlife, and the plentiful fish are a popular draw for anglers.

LAURENCE PARENT

LISA LYNCH

Blue Mesa Lake is a recreation mecca even after frigid temperatures freeze over the reservoir. Ice fishing and skating are popular, but the parks also offer ice climbing, cross country skiing, and snow shoeing. Other activities help fight cabin fever such as bird counts, and night sky programs.

LISA LYNCH

The fine art of fly fishing is practiced in the Gunnison River by anglers at East Portal, where Curecanti and Black Canyon come together. Gravel beds, slow pools, and steep cliffs combine to make for an incredible day of stalking brown and rainbow trout. The river is managed with special regulations to preserve the quality of fishing.

LISA LYNCH

Brown trout were introduced into the Gunnison River in the 1880s, and have come to thrive in the streams of the basin. Anglers also fish Blue Mesa for Kokanee salmon, Lake trout (or mackinaw) and rainbow trout.

*R*aucus afternoon winds make for windsurfing thrills on Blue Mesa Lake. Differential heating in
the Gunnison basin causes temperatures to rise through the morning at lower elevations. By afternoon the warm
air begins to rise, causing a void, or thermal low. Cool air from the mountains surrounding the basin rushes
downward to fill the void, creates potent tempests and drives the surfers and sailboats on a ride around the lake.
Winds are fickle, though, and there can be several causes for the gales.

E*ngine 278 once* *chugged over many miles* *of narrow gauge rails* *on the Denver and* *Rio Grande railroad.* *Built to pull trains* *through mountainous* *central Colorado,* *it ran on the line* *through the canyon* *from 1882 to 1949.* *Today it's poised* *on an original truss* *bridge at Cimarron.*

I*ola Basin bears the name of the hamlet* *that was once there. Trains loaded hundreds* *of cattle every year for eastern markets, and the hotels hosted anglers and sightseers every summer. Prehistoric* *people found the spot equally valuable, leaving behind evidence of their lives some 10,000 years ago.*

LISA LYNCH

Hermits Rest provides *impressive vistas of Morrow Point Reservoir and the Cimarron River basin in the distance. The lake covers the old railroad route, but of the ride Rudyard Kipling quipped, "We had been climbing for very many hours, when we entered a gorge, remote from the sun, where the rocks were two thousand feet sheer, and where a rock-splintered river roared and howled ten feet below a track which seemed to have been built on the simple principle of dropping miscellaneous dirt into the river and pinning a few rails atop. We seemed to be running into the bowels of the earth at the invitation of an irresponsible stream."*

SUGGESTED READING

BLOMQUIST, GERALDINE MOLETTIERE, AND PAUL B. BLOMQUIST. *Hiking the Gunnison River Basin.* Wayfinder Press, Ridgway, CO, 1996.

DECK, PETER R. *"The Utes Must Go," American Expansion and the Removal of a People.* Fulcrum Publishing, Golden, CO 2004.

HOUK, ROSE. *Curecanti National Recreation Area.* Western National Parks Association, Tucson, AZ, 1991.

LIGHTBOY, ANDY. *The Angling Guide to Colorado's Blue Mesa Reservoir.* North Cape Publications, Tustin, CA, 1995.

WIATROWSKI, CLAUDE. *Railroads of Colorado.* Voyageur Press, Stillwater, MN, 2002.

SUGGESTED WEB SITES

www.gunnisoncrestedbutte.com

There are two marinas on Blue Mesa lake which provide services to boaters. Blue Mesa is the largest reservoir in Colorado, 20 miles in length with 96 miles of shoreline. When full the lake holds nearly 941,000 acre feet (some 2.9 billion gallons) of water. Hydrologists measure an acre foot as one acre of ground covered with water one foot deep. Blue Mesa Dam, along with Morrow Point and Crystal Dams downstream, work in concert to provide water storage, generate electricity and recreation for millions each year. The U.S. Bureau of Reclamation administers the dams, and together they are called the Wayne N. Aspinall Unit. Aspinall was a Colorado Congressman and strong proponent of water development in the state.

LISA LYNCH

Glistening waters surround the Elk Creek Marina, which provides many boater services. There are several boat access points on Blue Mesa Lake, but Morrow Point and Crystal Lakes lie deep in the canyon. Boating there is limited to hand-carried craft.

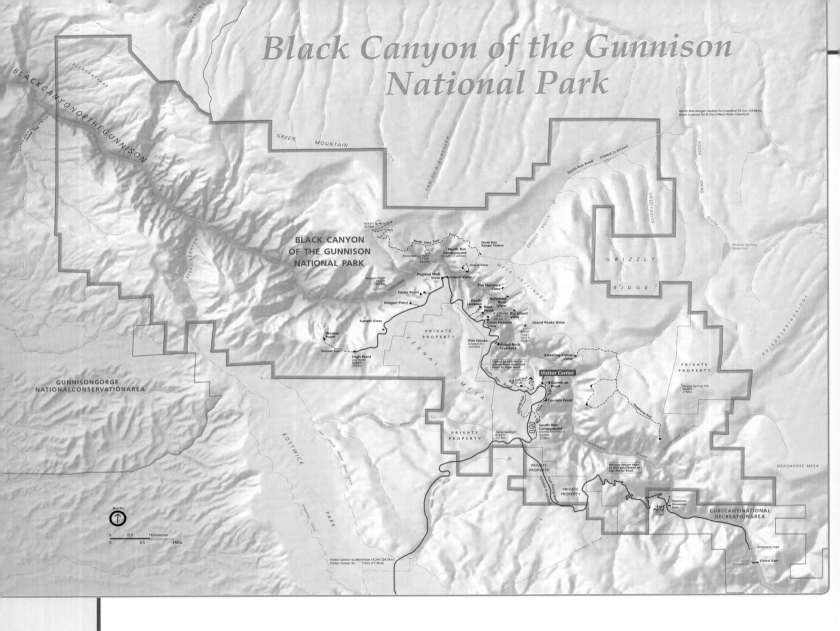

Black Canyon of the Gunnison National Park

JUNIOR RANGER PROGRAM

BE A JUNIOR PARK RANGER!

Help take care of America's Treasures!

Anyone between the ages of 5 and 12 can become a Junior Park Ranger at Black Canyon of the Gunnison National Park and Curecanti National Recreation Area. There are challenging activities in our Junior Ranger Book that you can do when you visit the Park. Learn how to care for these places and all of our national parks.

Stop by any visitor center for more information and to pick up your free Junior Ranger Book.

Western National Parks Association (WNPA)

WESTERN NATIONAL PARKS ASSOCIATION (WNPA) is a non-profit membership organization authorized by Congress to aid and promote educational and scientific activities within more than 70 park sites in the American southwest. WNPA has roots that stretch back to 1938 when a need was recognized for continuing the public's interest and education in their national parks. Since then, they have helped millions to understand more of their natural and cultural history. They publish numerous trail guides, books and other materials that would otherwise be unavailable to the public.

CONTACT INFORMATION

Call us at:
(970) 641-2337

Fax us at:
(970) 641-3127

Write to us at:
National Park Service
102 Elk Creek
Gunnison, CO 81230

Visit us at our Website:
Black Canyon of the Gunnison:
www.nps.gov/blca
Curecanti National Recreation Area:
www.nps.gov/cure

Curecanti National Recreation Area

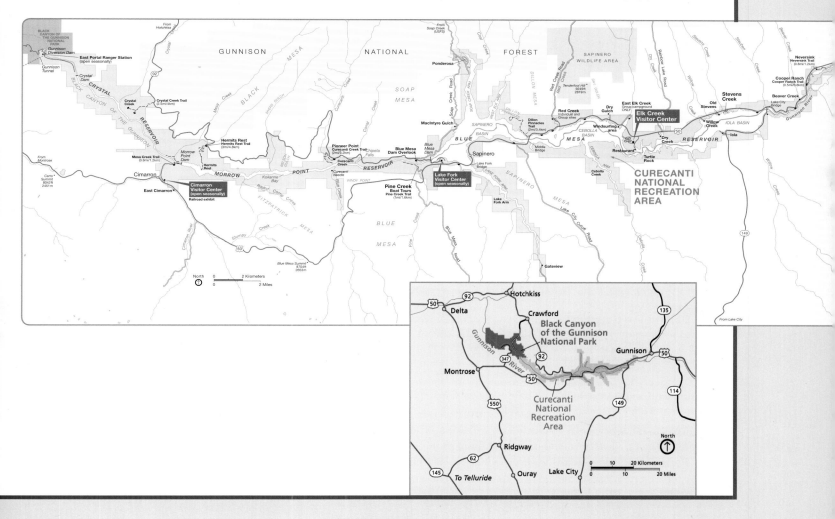

A Look to the Future

When Mark Warner dreamed of a National Park, he did not know then that his idea would eventually be realized. Through a collaborative process, the Black Canyon of the Gunnison is now protected in three segments. The upper reaches are preserved in Curecanti National Recreation Area, set aside in 1965 at the time when the Bureau of Reclamation was constructing the dams on the Gunnison River. As the century drew to a close, a group effort brought about the creation of the Gunnison Gorge Conservation and Wilderness Areas, and the Black Canyon of the Gunnison National Park in 1999.

The effort to continue Warner's dream of preserving these resources goes on, as concerns over endangered species, river water for the canyon's habitat, and air quality require constant vigilance. Black Canyon is a place that holds great power to move people, but only if we today ensure the preservation of all of its parts, allowing its rhythms of life to proceed, will it be here to inspire people in the future.

LAURENCE PARENT

Dawn brings a new day at Gunnison Point. Rise early to ponder the silence most commonly found in the morning.